COVID-19

A PHYSICIAN'S TAKE ON THE EXAGGERATED FEAR OF THE CORONAVIRUS

$7.95

COVID-19

A PHYSICIAN'S TAKE ON THE EXAGGERATED FEAR OF THE CORONAVIRUS

Jeffrey I. Barke, M.D.

THE AMERICAS GROUP

The Americas Group
520 S. Sepulveda Blvd, Suite 204
Los Angeles, California 90049-3534 U.S.A.

ISBN
978-0-935047-94-3

Library of Congress Control Number:
2020913068

Description: First edition. | Los Angeles, CA :
The Americas Group, 2020. | Includes index. |
Summary: "This book of brief essays methodically examines the major Covid-19 issues to
determine what is fact and what is myth. It is
written by a family physician who pointedly
differs on the threat posed by Covid-19 to
the American people, then challenges current
conventional wisdom on what should be done
about the schools, the economy and public
activity with reason, honesty and scientific
findings."- Provided by publisher.

Printed in India by
AEGEAN OFFSET PRINTING, LTD.

TABLE OF
CONTENTS

FOREWORD

THE TALMUD, JU-DAISM'S second holiest work after the Bible, a repository of law, folklore, and wisdom the size of an encyclopedia, contains an amazing statement: "The best physicians go to hell."

Now, why would a holy work say such a thing about physicians, those who are arguably engaged in the holiest work of all — saving human lives? Moreover, why would it say such a thing about "the best" of them?

The answer is the ancient rabbis understood how tempting it can be for a physician, more than for the members of other professions, to think of himself — and for others to think of him — as a god.

I can say with certainty that the Talmudic principle does not apply to Dr. Jeffrey Barke. He is certainly one of the best physicians, but he knows that no doctor, not even those who run the CDC or the FDA or who edit the *New England Journal of Medicine* or *The Lancet*, is a god. That is why he is prepared to challenge conventional medical wisdom when doing so is warranted by the facts.

He has taken a hard look at the lockdowns implemented in America and in almost every other country at the behest of doctors in response to the novel coronavirus known as Covid-19, and he sees a mistake the likes of which no one alive at this time has seen.

Unlike most of his colleagues, he not only sees the price people pay because of the virus, he sees the price paid because of the lockdown: the impoverishment of hundreds of millions of people around the world, the impoverishment and near-impoverishment of countless Americans, the increase in depression, suicide, children's loss of education, family tension, increased drug use, recovering addicts returning to their addiction, people delaying or forgoing necessary medical treatments and much more. And he sees the political turmoil that inactivity, economic depression and loss of income inevitably lead to.

Also, unlike many of his colleagues, he has the courage to advocate medical treatments that work, irrespective of what the medical establishment has pronounced, not because of science, but because of politics.

The combination of medical expertise, courage, and wisdom is very rare. We have all three traits in Jeffrey Barke. That's why he needs to be heard.

And that's why I think the ancient rabbis would have said, "Here's one physician who will go to Heaven."

I certainly think so.

Dennis Prager
Radio talk show host,
lecturer and author
whose intellect and integrity
have influenced millions of
lives.

INTRODUCTION

THERE ARE MANY great traditions in American political life. Freedom of speech is perhaps the most fundamental. That freedom not only permits the widest possible expression of views but encourages dissent from conventional wisdom no matter how broadly or how firmly the majority view is held.

How to deal with the Covid-19 in the United States is one of those subjects that seems to have trapped our political leaders between the opinions of public health specialists and those of the nation's most prominent media personalities.

But just as the four physicians who signed the American Declaration of Independence — and pledged their lives, their fortunes and their sacred honor to renounce the rule of King George III in the American colonies — so Dr. Jeffrey I. Barke, a family physician in Newport

Beach, California, begs to differ in many ways with the conventional wisdom concerning the threat of Covid-19 to the American population.

In a series of essays on the following pages, many first published online, Dr. Barke methodically examines the major Covid-19 issues to determine what is fact and what is myth. He buttresses his analyses with reason, honesty and scientific findings that go against so much of what the public has been led to believe from public officials and the media in the first half of 2020.

Readers are urged to examine for themselves whether his ideas make sense. Keep an open mind. Be part of that other great American tradition that believes in unbridled and fair debate to arrive at new conclusions.

Godfrey Harris
Public Policy Consultant
and Managing Editor of
The Americas Group

FIRST, DO NO HARM —
PRIMUM NON NOCERE

HIPPOCRATES WAS A Greek physician who lived some 400 years before the common era. He is often referred to as the father of modern medicine because he was one of the first to describe his medical observations in a scientific manner.

He is perhaps best known for his dictum expessed in Latin: *Primum non nocere* — or, "First, do no harm." It is part of the Hippocratic oath that is still attested to by medical school graduates.

Politicians should be administered a similar oath

when they take office. If they were, they might not have done all the questionable things we are dealing with in the current Covid-19 situation.

There is no doubt that Covid-19 is a dangerous virus to the elderly and the frail (and, early on, to those who live in New York City). But the fact is that the overall reaction to the virus has caused more harm than the virus itself.

As more and more data become available, it is clear that the resulting fatality rate from this virus will be around 0.2%. That is in the ballpark of a bad influenza season. It is also twenty times lower than originally assumed by the World Health Organization (WHO).

The fatality rate for Covid-19 patients coming out of nursing homes and assisted living facilities account for close to 50% of all deaths in the United States; younger Americans have a much lower fatality rate from this disease.

In fact, the average age of Covid's faatal victims in most countries is more than 80. For Americans under the age of 25 there is a greater risk of being killed in an automobile accident than from Covid-19. Despite this, we have closed our schools and continue to cogitate about how and when to reopen them.

Moreover, the Covid-19 death toll itself is also now coming into question as the official figures do not differentiate death *from* Covid-19 vs. death *with* Covid-19.

In addition, we are learning that many presumed Covid-19 deaths had no laboratory confirmation and may have been coded as such to capture increased reimbursement from various government agencies.

I believe that when the history books are written about this pandemic, it will show that our reaction to this virus was a great mistakes . Worse, the continuation of our initial response to the virus is no longer just a mistake, it is bordering on malice.

With more than 30 million Americans unemployed at the height of the initial reaction to the spread of the disease and with estimates that 40% of those will not have jobs to return to, the economic devastation initially crippled America and the world. This self-inflicted economic wound has also caused an almost complete shutdown of the U.S. outpatient healthcare system.

Doctors from all over the country report devastating consequences to their patients. Recently I co-authored with Simone Gold, M.D., J.D., a letter to President Trump highlighting this aspect of the healthcare crisis. The letter can be reviewed at *www.adoctoraday.com*.

Two days after the White House received this letter, Dr. Anthony Fauci of the President's Coronavirus Task Force changed his message to the public:

Stay-at-home orders intended to curb the spread of the coronavirus could cause "irreparable damage."

A psychiatrist reported that his office volume is down by 80% and yet his prescriptions for benzodiazepines (Valium, Xanax, Ativan) are the highest in his career. Patients who require frequent visits to stay functional are not coming into his office for fear of contracting the virus.

A cardiologist reports that routine echocardiograms and other non-invasive cardiac testing protocols are not being administered because these procedures have been declared non-essential. Patients are afraid to visit a doctor's office.

A gastroenterologist reported that routine cancer screening colonoscopies have stopped altogether, and a gynecologist reported that cancer-screening pap smears and mammograms have ceased.

I am personally aware of

a 61-year-old patient who died of intestinal obstruction because he feared going into his doctor's office. Instead, he suffered at home, ultimately succumbing to sepsis.

These examples are being repeated across our country with devastating consequences. False information about waiting for a vaccination, the need for widespread testing, mask-wearing and potential asymptomatic spread of Covid-19 fill the airways and stoke unnecessary fear among the American citizenry.

Winston Churchill once noted that "Fear is a reaction, courage a decision." Maybe it is time for us to remember Dr. Hippocrates' statement from long ago: "First, do no harm."

It would go a long way to putting the current situation on the right track, not just by our doctors but by our elected officials as well.

IMMUNE
SYSTEMS
MATTER

PLANS AND DEMANDS for school reopenings are coming in fast and furious from government and nongovernment organizations alike. Some are hundreds of pages long, requiring a phalanx of Ph.D.s to sort through the details before implementation.

What seems universally clear is that no one is taking into account that the vast majority of us have immensely powerful immune systems that play a critical role in keeping us healthy and alive.

One plan calls for using sanitizing spray on all classroom surfaces multiple times per day; that children use hand sanitizer upon entering and exiting the classroom; and that all children and staff wear masks for the entire school day and, of course, ensure social distancing. The bureaucrats at the CDC would be proud of the results.

But all of these "specialists" have ignored the fact that from the day we are born we are assaulted by germs — by the millions, if not billions. Our very existence is dependent on a robust immune system — that is, the ability of our bodies to fight off any invasion of bacteria, viruses, fungus, mold or other pathogens. Fortunately, we were created with a powerful internal standing army of cells ready to protect us in each battle and capable of winning most wars.

In order for our immune system to be prepared for those battles, it has to train regularly and bring new recruits to the effort. Even before we are born, our immune system is exposed to germs and is working to protect us.

The result is that our bodies create germ-specific special ops fighters to defeat a variety of enemies that life throws at us. Each time we are exposed to new or old germs, our immune system grows smarter and stronger.

It is healthy and necessary for our very survival to be exposed to different germs and to recover to fight another day. If we purposely prevent such exposure, we may gain in the short term, but we may also lose in devastating ways in the long term.

You may remember seeing on TV an episode of *Seinfeld* titled, "The Bubble Boy." In this 30-minute story a boy needed to live inside a plastic bubble because he did not have a functioning immune system. It didn't end well for the "Bubble Boy" when his germ-free bubble was violated and he was exposed to germs.

Modern society has gone overboard with deploying antibacterial soaps, lotions and cleaning products. They indiscriminately kill germs, yes, but they also wipe out the good bacteria that help maintain a strong and diverse microbiome. "Kills up to 99.9% of common germs," promises the label of one brand of hand sanitizer.

Everyone has a microbiome, a collection of more than 100 trillion (!) microbes that live on and in our bodies, the majority in our large (and clearly crowded) intestine. The more diverse your individual microbiome, the healthier you are.

Research indicates that early exposure to a variety of microbes may help lower the risk of developing conditions like asthma, allergies and even infectious diseases. Think of it this way: If you exercise regularly and your body is fit, you are less likely to be injured, be overweight, have cardiovascular disease or suffer from diabetes. When you stop exercising, your level of fitness declines, along with all the benefits.

Your immune system works in the same way: Stimulate it regularly, such as when a child plays in the dirt, and you are more likely to win the battles against dangerous germs and viruses, including Covid-19.

With COVID-19, we have gone "Bubble Boy" sterilization crazy, and it is not helping us. We now sanitize everything: bus seats, door handles, gas pumps, purchased products, our bodies.

We are cleaning our homes (and some offices) as if they were an extension of a hospital's ICU. I have one patient who told me he comes home from the market, takes off all of his clothes outside, hoses himself off, puts the clothes in a bag, and then takes a hot shower.

The fear of Covid-19 has driven us to impossible and unhealthful behavior.

SIZE MATTERS IN SCIENCE AND COMMON SENSE

California Governor Gavin Newsom recently issued an edict that everyone, with a few exceptions, must wear masks in public to protect against the spread of Covid-19.

A lively debate immediately ensued as to whether he had the authority to issue such an order. But what is more important, even if it is established that he has the authority, does mandating the wearing of masks make common sense?

Consider just this: The virus particles associated with Covid-19 are about 0.12 of a micron in size. Why does size matter? Because the pores in a typical surgical mask can filter objects no smaller than 3.0 microns.

An N95 mask, if fitted properly to the individual wearer, can filter objects down to 0.1 to 0.3 of a micron. A 0.12 micron Covid-19 virus particle will pass through an ordinary surgical mask easily as well as any homemade cloth product. It is the equivalent of erecting a chain-link fence to keep out mosquitoes.

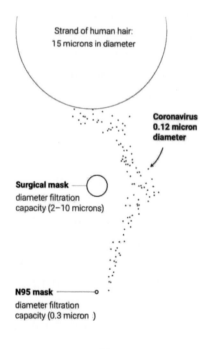

Strand of human hair:
15 microns in diameter

**Coronavirus
0.12 micron
diameter**

Surgical mask
diameter filtration
capacity (2–10 microns)

N95 mask
diameter filtration
capacity (0.3 micron)

There have been several studies about preventing the transmission of influenza and the common cold by wearing surgical masks. The studies concluded they were ineffective. That's why we are not told to wear them during flu season. There are no studies yet related to masks and Covid-19 — only anecdotal evidence which is mixed.

Fair enough, but a lot of readers will have heard that Covid-19 is mostly carried in droplets of mucus or spittle and any face covering will stop that. There is some truth to this. A sneeze or cough containing Covid-19 may be partially blocked by a mask or bandana. The science is inconclusive on the extent to which a sneeze or cough can get through these protective coverings.

But note this: As moisture builds up inside a face covering, its filtering ability drops precipitously.

Moreover, if Covid-19 virus particles are now trapped and building up inside a face covering, it could be re-infecting the mask wearer, going from the mouth into the nose. This does not even account for the fact that every time the mask is adjusted or touched the virus may be transferred to the wearer's fingers or hands and whatever is subsequently touched. And, please, never exercise in a mask — even a brisk walk in a mask can lower your oxygen saturation, cause headaches and put your health at risk.

Why then does a surgeon wear a mask during an operation? It is not to prevent a viral infection impacting the patient. It is to prevent the surgeons' and nurses' spittle, while talking during surgery, from getting into an open wound and causing a nosocomial bacterial infection. It is also to prevent pieces of tissue splattering into the surgeons' and nurses' mouths.

If there were no need to talk during surgery, there would be little need to wear a mask — other than splattering tissue. Furthermore, a 2008 study of 53 surgeons by A. Beder showed reduced oxygenation and increased pulse rate after an hour of mask wearing during surgery.

But if I'm six feet away from another person, am I safe? There is zero science behind six feet of separation. The Europeans and Africans maintain a meter (about three feet) of separation. But why not four feet or eight feet? Because six feet was thought to be an easily remembered and calibrated number.

It is a guess that most people can't project the particles of a sneeze or cough further than six feet. Common sense tells us that if you are not near an infected person you are less likely to get infected —

which is why it made no sense when the Governor closed outdoor spaces such as parks and beaches. But since when have politicians been required to apply common sense?

Okay, back to size — the size of children! Little people are at very low risk of contracting Covid-19. In Orange County, California, we have had no deaths in children and only 20 deaths in the United States, all of whom had a serious pre-existing condition.

The CDC's website reports the risk of death in children from Covid-19 as 0.00%. Children have a 50 times higher risk of drowning and a much higher risk of being killed in an auto accident than dying from Covid-19. So why all the fuss about opening schools?

Fear is a powerful facilitator of public opinion, especially when it is in the hands of organized labor. Teachers' union demands are driving this narrative. The concern of school children wearing masks is that a little one might be able to spread the virus to an at-risk teacher.

I have a patient who has Stage 4 breast cancer and is undergoing chemotherapy. This depletes her immune system, putting her at high risk of getting an opportunistic infection such as Covid-19.

We can either protect and if necessary isolate *her* or we can mask everyone who lives near her or visits wherever she goes. Common sense tells us what to do. More important, we have multiple studies that show there is little evidence that children can asymptomatically transmit the virus.

The WHO indicated as such in June when Maria Van Kerkhove, M.D., the technical lead for the WHO's pandemic response unit, said: "... asymptomatic transmission appears to be very rare." Yes, political pressure caused her to walk back her comments the following day. The politics of health-care is getting ugly.

So what should we do? Mask up if you *feel* you must, but don't blame it on science. A school child should never wear a mask and socially distancing among children also makes no sense.

A healthy society protects the most vulnerable and isolates those who are sick. Covid-19 poses only influenza-like risk to the young and the healthy under 65 years of age.

We should size up this pandemic properly, ignore the sensation-mongering headlines, and act with a touch of old fashion common sense.

BETTER TO BE GOOD
OR LUCKY?

AS EXPECTED BY most observers, the number of cases of Covid-19 continues to increase across the country. There are primarily three reasons for the spike in cases:

1. More testing is being performed.
2. People are moving about as the economy opens up.
3. Massive protests and riots across the country.

The net statistic that will

be used to frighten the American people will be the increase in hospitalizations that will follow the expanded number of cases. Days or weeks after hospitalizations grow in number, even more deaths are likely to arise.

What will not be reported in the gloomy news roundups is the fact that we now have effective treatments for Covid-19. More appalling, many doctors and hospital systems are refusing to use these effective therapeutics.

Dr. Vladimir Zelenko, a New York family medicine physician, has pioneered a treatment strategy that works well but is still shunned by most of the medical profession and ignored by the mainstream news media. Dr. Zelenko said this on Dennis Prager's radio show of July 10, 2020:

> *I don't care what 'they' say anymore, I would rather speak directly to the American peo-*

ple and tell them I have some very good news for [them]. We have an answer to the terrible infection, we have a very effective way of treating it. In the high-risk groups there is a 99.3% survival [rate] and a 84% reduction in hospitalizations. There is also a 100% survival rate in low-risk patients when treatment is started in the first five days [after the onset of] an infection.

One of the key reasons for the increase in hospitalizations has also not been widely reported. The increase is in part due to the reopening of hospitals to elective surgeries and procedures. These had previously been categorized as non-essential by many state authorities.

Hospitals are also using ICU wards to isolate Covid-19 cases and not for the usual ICU acuity care. In addition, some of the ICU admissions are for relatively routine, not Covid-19, hospitalizations.

The early treatment of

Covid-19 patients with mild symptoms has proven over-whelmingly effective. In Texas, Dr. Richard Bartlett has a 100% track record of no deaths with his treatment of Covid-19. As part of his protocol, he uses an inexpensive inhaled asthma steroid called budesonide. This treats the pulmonary inflam-mation that is often the culprit in the death of patients with Covid-19.

Both hydroxycholoquine and budesonide are only a frac-tion of the cost of Remdesivir with its multiple thousands of dollars per dosage. Is there a fi-nancial incentive in maligning the cheaper treatment alterna-tives? One has to suspect that.

Dr. Zelenko's protocol of hydroxychloroquine + zinc + azithromycin has been made publicly toxic because Presi-dent Trump mentioned just the first ingredient during a brief-ing on March 19, 2020. Yet a study released on July 2nd by the Henry Ford Health Systems in Detroit showed a significant reduction in death of over 2,500 hospitalized patients using the Zelenko cocktail of medicines.

For reasons that are not clear, the national media has refused to acknowledge this hydroxychloroquine study result, perhaps for fear that President Trump might be given some credit for promoting the drug. Information on the study can be found on the Internet under "Henry Ford Health study."

So, if you are someone who has recently tested positive for the Covid-19 virus, there is great hope for you. The challenge is to find a doctor who is not influenced by politics. If you are not currently positive for Covid-19, there is a lot you should consider to maximize your ability to fight off this infection if it comes your way.

First and most important, take excellent care of yourself, which includes: Eating healthful food, exercising daily, keeping your weight down, and taking some immune-improvement supplements.

Please check with your own physician prior to taking any medication or supplements. Here is a list I recommend to my patients:

- Vitamin-C 3,000 mg daily
- Vitamin-D3 5,000 IU daily
- Zinc 50 mg daily
- Magnesium 400 mg daily
- Selenium 100 ug daily

In addition, stay well hydrated and avoid sugar as well as excessive alcohol. Get plenty of fresh air and sunshine, sleep six to eight hours each night, and most important manage your stress.

Do not rely on being lucky to either avoid getting Covid-19 or surviving the infection should you contract it. Prepare yourself by being healthy and, if needed, seek out a doctor who understands that effective treatments are available outside of a hospital setting.

NOT DYING IS BAD FOR HEADLINES — COVID-19 CASES VS. DEATH

AS WE TRAVEL the bumpy Covid-19 path back to normalcy, you would never know that we are headed in the right direction.

Teasers on television and headlines in newspapers report a "surge" in new cases of Covid-19 as well as hospitalizations; the

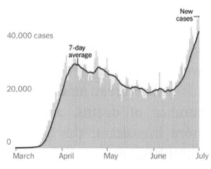

New reported cases by day in the United States

the teasers and headlines, of course, fail to mention that the most important measure of our progress in getting ahead of the virus is the number of *deaths* recorded. The fact that the rate of fatalities to infection is very low now is seldom if ever mentioned.

After weeks of unnecessarily shutting down our economy and the travesty of closing schools, it was certain that cases of Covid-19 would spike as we reopened society - *duh*.

When the massive protests and riots around the county over the succeeding weeks are taken into consideration, it ought to be no surprise that cases are increasing. It is important to remember that the purpose of "flattening the curve" was to delay cases and death from Covid-19 to a future date when our healthcare capacity was no longer threatened with being overwhelmed.

The great news is that the number of deaths, and perhaps more important, the fatality rate (the likelihood of death from infection), has plummeted. Why? Because this virus tends to be very mild in the young and healthy — the cohort that has been most susceptible to infection of late.

The CDC data show that as of July 1, 2020, death in people younger than 25 is less than 170 out of a total of 120,000. It is almost non-pronounceable to state a fatality rate — too many zeros after the decimal point.

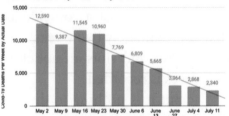

Covid-19 Deaths By Week They Occurred

My point is this: If you are young and healthy, you have nothing to fear from the coronavirus except the fear-mongering from the media.

The average age of the "new cases" now spiking is 31 years old — similar to the age, by most estimates, of the protesters and rioters recently in the streets. I looked carefully at news coverage and videos of the protests and riots across the country and couldn't find many participants who looked 65 years old or older.

Moreover, I couldn't see much social distancing going on either! Yet, we are told that reopening restaurants, bars and retail stores — most of which had tried to arrange for social distancing and some of which required masks — is the source of the spike in new cases. I guess it is just a coincidence that approximately two weeks after the protests and riots an uptick in new cases is recorded.

But it is nothing to die for: The reason we continue to see a drop in deaths from Covid-19 is because a younger group is being exposed to the virus and we are much better at treating it.

Hydroxychloroquine + Z-pack + zinc have proven effective for early and mild infections. Doctors are also now using anti-inflammatory steroids (Dexamethasone and Prednisone) earlier and more aggressively in treatments.

The length of hospital stays for Covid-19 are also now dropping. Early on I wrote that the Covid-19 fatality rate will turn out to be in the ballpark of a bad influenza season. This is now becoming the case. The more we test, the lower the fatality rate as well. Approximately 98.6% of infected people will experience either no symptoms or mild symptoms and approximately 99.85% of all infected cases will recover.

A healthy society protects its most vulnerable members and isolates the sick while allowing the healthy individuals to go about their lives. Let's celebrate the drop in deaths and stop sensationalizing the "new cases" of Covid-19 as worthy of another shutdown.

NOTES/QUESTIONS

DEFUND THE POLICE: WRONG TARGET, RIGHT IDEA

THE MANY CALLS to defund the nation's police forces make no sense at all — another slogan without definition, another emotional reaction without thought.

Yet, the idea of defunding government agencies that do not deliver the public services they promise makes a lot of sense. Underperforming government schools and their powerful unions would be a good place to start.

The failure of government-owned educational services in the United States is irrefutable. Study after study has shown that millions of American kids graduate below their grade level in math and ELA (English language arts). Embarrassingly, we spend more money on this type of schooling than almost any other country. Talk about value for money; we get none.

Let's get specific. I served as one of five elected members of the Los Alamitos Unified School District's Board of Trustees for 12 years. It was one of the top performing districts in Orange County, California.

During my time on the board, we routinely analyzed the results of California's annual required standardized tests, principally the California Assessment of Student Performance and Progress (CAASPP) in two basic categories: math and ELA. The 2018–19 results show that 48.9% of students were below grade level for ELA and 60.27% below grade level for math.

These results are even more depressing for students in minority communities. As you can see from the following graphs, there has been little change in student performance over time:

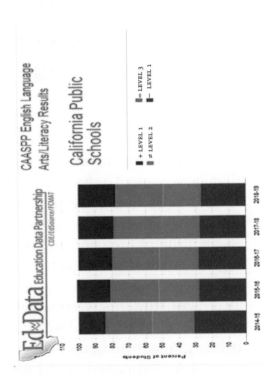

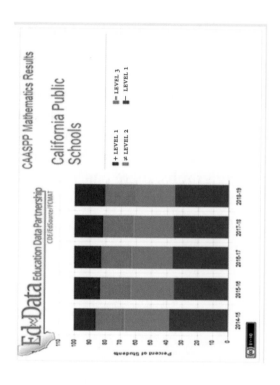

How can anyone argue that government education in California is doing the job? In my school district in 2018–19 — an affluent area encompassing the cities of Seal Beach, Los Alamitos and Rossmoor — 19.35% of students were below grade level in ELA and 42.67% below grade level in math.

I was appalled, and I realized that to argue that only inner-city schools are underperforming is a fallacy. When I first saw our abysmal math scores, I offered three recommendations that were summarily rejected by the school district's professional administrators and even by my fellow board members.

1. The first proposal I made was to make participation in elective activities, such as athletic teams and performing arts programs, contingent on achieving grade level scores on standardized tests. We would provide extra help and tutoring for students as needed. I was told we could not do this — it would be viewed as discriminatory by other students, teachers and coaches. I was also told the teachers' union would never allow this, as it could impact teacher employment. Furthermore, I was told that if not for these elective activi-

ties, some students would simply drop out of school. I argued that this would encourage better academics and put elective activities in perspective.

2. My second recommendation was to provide a financial incentive to teachers to increase student achievement. I was told this would not be legal because teacher compensation is a negotiated item with the union and our "Uniform Compensation System" is a law that must be followed. Under the law, teacher compensation is based solely on years of employment and educational achievements — never on competency. In an era where we are re-examining police policies dictated by police unions (keeping disciplinary records hidden from the public, for

example), we should be re-examining this job protection provision as well.

3. My final recommendation was for the district to provide vouchers to every student who is below grade level. These could be used with a private tutor or with one of our own teachers offering tutoring services. I was told that we could not do this because it would imply that our own teachers are not capable of teaching our own students, and it would cause undesired pushback from the union. Let's not be unnecessarily disruptive, I was told.

Los Alamitos High School math scores continue to be abysmal right along with the rest of California and the country. I doubt that parents even realize that this failure is occurring. We keep doing the same thing over and over yet expect different results — the best definition of insanity we have, whether Albert Einstein said it or not.

Those on the political left are correct about defunding — they just need to redirect their defunding energies to deserving government targets.

RIOTING MUST NOT BE ALLOWED TO DEFINE A NEW AMERICA

EMBEDDED IN THE fabric of America's freedoms is the right of the people to "peacefully assenble" and to "petition the Government for a redress of grievances."

Nothing in the Constitution, however, gives anyone the right to riot, loot and burn down any part of any city. Yet in some cities across America, there seems to be an assumption of an unwritten right to do just that.

Our founders correctly believed that all men are created equal, that they are endowed by their Creator with certain unalienable rights, and that among these are life, liberty and the pursuit of happiness.

The rights of George Floyd, the Minneapolis resident who was slain by the police in 2020, were snuffed out. The officer who was responsible for this act is now awaiting a murder trial along with those who stood silently by.

Justice is underway. Its wheels may turn slowly, but an old saying has it that they grind exceedingly fine. That requires us to have patience and trust in an imperfect system that by all accounts is considered one of the best in the world. It is a system that can be changed by a deliberative process undertaken by duly empowered government representatives. It is not designed for the emotional tantrums of an out-of-control, radical mob.

At no time is our civil society more at risk than when lawlessness is encouraged and allowed to overtake our justice system. "No justice, no peace" is an often heard rallying cry of those protesting in the streets.

Except whose justice is in question and by what measure is peace achieved?

The constant drumbeat from those on the political left holds that America is endemically racist, that our "systemic and institutional" racism has been harmful to any progress or healing.

"Repeat a lie often enough, and it becomes the truth" is an axiom of propaganda often attributed to the Nazis' Joseph Goebbels. As I look at it, The New York Times 1619 Project is an example of this type of propaganda.

I have been a volunteer reserve deputy for a local law enforcement agency for many years. I was recently deployed as a tactical medic for a SWAT team to help with local protests/riots. In my many years involved in law enforcement, I have never seen "systemic or institutional" racism.

Our SWAT team is multethnic and multi-racial. I have never viewed my team members through any lens other than competency. I read a recent opinion piece where the author stated:

A majority of white Americans still cannot come to terms with what black people have known forever: Racism is systemic, systematic and nowhere near gone.

There are many black conservatives who differ, and we had a two-term black president who got the majority white vote overwhelmingly.

There are bad apples in every profession and every walk of life. It is the nature of human existence. We must not confuse the few with the majority. We must not allow peaceful and righteous protesters to be overtaken by radical groups that use the cover of an unjust act to further their own socio-political agenda.

Peaceful protesters and politicians must speak out loudly against this anarchy. Where is justice and where is peace for those store-owners whose establishments are looted and torched? Where is justice and where is peace for the innocent bystanders who are injured or killed? Where is justice and where is peace for injured or killed law enforcement officers taking a stand to protect innocent life and property? Where is the outcry when a church in Washington, D.C., built in the 1800s is torched?

The path forward must include an intolerance of lawless acts of violence and looting. We must use the full extent of local law enforcement, bolstered as necessary by the National Guard, to shut down the riots immediately and return civility to the streets.

Martin Luther King, Jr. once said:

> *The limitation of riots, moral questions aside, is that they cannot win and their participants know it. Hence, rioting is not revolutionary but reactionary because it invites defeat. It involves an emotional catharsis, but it must be followed by a sense of futility.*

That futility must be followed by an open dialogue where feelings are discussed but facts drive policy. Racial division is a useful tool for those who want a radical progressive change to our government institutions.

Saul Alinsky, the author and political theorist, knew this well when he stated:

The despair is there; now it's up to us to go in and rub raw the sores of discontent.

Those who came after America's founders had a different vision for America. They believed protecting "one nation under God, with liberty and justice for all."

I hope most Americans today feel the same.

JEFFREY I. BARKE, M.D.

Dr. Barke is a board certified primary care physician who has a concierge practice based in Newport Beach, California.

He completed his medical school training and family practice residency at the University of California Irvine and earned his undergraduate degree at the University of Southern California.

During his more than 20 years as a physician, he has served as an associate clinical professor at the University of California Irvine's Medical School, chairman of the Family Medicine Department at Hoag Memorial Hospital, on the board of directors of the Orange County Medical Association and as medical director of Pathways to Independence.

Dr. Barke was elected to three, four-year terms as a member of the Los Alamitos Unified School District Board of Education and is currently a member of the Board of Directors of the Roosmoor Community Services District. Dr. Barke is a co-founder and current board chair of Orange County Classical Academy, a free public charter school in Orange, California. Dr. Barke also serves as a reserve deputy and tactical physician for the Orange County Sheriff's Department.

Dr. Barke co-authored *The Essential Diet Planning Kit* (with Godfrey Harris) in 2005. He has appeared multiple times on the *Dennis Prager Show*, the *Larry Elder Show*, and on *Fox News Special Report* with Bret Baier.

He is married to his high school sweetheart, Mari Barke, who is the vice president of the Orange County Board of Education. They have two adult children, both of whom live out of state.

ACKNOWLEDGMENTS

I wish to thank my wife of over 30 years, **Mari Barke,** for her support, ideas and tolerance of my new social media activities. She is also the photographer of the head shot of me that appears with my biography.

My daughter, **Allie Barke**, played an important role in helping with social media and creative content. She also designed our logo (see at the end of this section) and maintains my website:

www.rxforliberty.com

Thank you also to my son, **Sam Barke**, for pushing me to stay in the fight with courage.

Special appreciation goes to my business partner, **Dr. Kenneth Cheng**, for allowing my passion to flourish and to the staff of **Personal Care Physicians** of Newport Beach, California, for fielding calls to the office - not all of which are supportive!

I am grateful to **Dennis Prager** and **Larry Elder** for inviting me to share my views on their radio shows and for writing the book's Foreword (Prager) and saying those nice words on the book's backcover (Elder).

I was taught that there is no such thing as good writing, only good rewriting, so thank you to **Godfrey Harris** and **The Americas Group**'s stable of specialists, especially Editor **Art Detman,** without whose help this book would not be possible.

Thank you also to the *American Thinker* (www.americanthinker.com) for publishing most of these essays. Special appreciation to **Earick Ward** for co-authoring some of the pieces in the book and supporting my efforts to give our ideas a wider audience.

Finally, it has been quite a bumpy ride for the United States over the past several months. I have tried to put forward a common sense approach to dealing with Covid-19 issues and the societal upheaval that was in part spawned by the pandemic.

I have been called a hero by some and a quack by others — my home county is fractured by vehemently held opposing views like never before. The coming weeks leading up to the Presidential election will likely be filled with more turmoil.

I will continue to write and speak as time permits and express my thoughts on social media. I have been humbled to have been given an opportunity to have my voice heard across America and carrie into foreign lands.

I am hopeful God will bless me with continued energy, strength and wisdom to lead with facts and science and help America.

I am looking forward to feedback from readers in the hopes of improving my message to better communicate common sense to close the widening gap between healthcare and politics.

Dr. Barke's blog can be accessed at
RxForLiberty.com

INDEX